Dr. Jekyll and Mr. Hyde

based on the classic story by
Robert Louis Stevenson

SCHOLASTIC INC.
New York   Toronto   London   Auckland   Sydney
Mexico City   New Delhi   Hong Kong

**Cover illustration by
Balvis Rubess**

**Interior illustrations by
Paul Didier**

"Dr. Jekyll and Mr. Hyde" adapted by Steven Otfinoski from DR. JEKYLL AND MR. HYDE by Robert Louis Stevenson. Adaptation originally published in *Scholastic Action* magazine, November 4–18, 1994. Adaptation copyright © 1994 by Scholastic Inc. All rights reserved.

"The Invisible Man" adapted from THE INVISIBLE MAN by H.G. Wells. Adaptation originally published in *Scholastic Scope* magazine, March 21, 1997. Adaptation copyright © 1997 by Scholastic Inc. All rights reserved.

ISBN 0-439-31273-6

7 8 9 10   23   13 12

Characters

Narrator

John Utterson, Jekyll's friend and lawyer

Dr. Henry Jekyll, an English doctor

Jane Manners, Jekyll's girlfriend

Edward Hyde, Jekyll's evil side

Poole, Jekyll's butler

Sir Rodney Carew, Jekyll's neighbor

Minnie, Jekyll's maid

Police Officer 1

Police Officer 2

Scene 1

Narrator: The scene is the home of Dr. Henry Jekyll in London, England. The time is the 1880s. Dr. Jekyll is spending the evening with his girlfriend, Jane Manners, and his friend John Utterson.

Utterson: Henry, tell me what you've been up to these days in that secret laboratory of yours.

Jekyll: Oh, nothing much.

Jane *(smiling)*: Henry is very quiet about his work, John. He doesn't even tell me much about what he's doing.

Utterson: I'm sure that will change once you two are married. *(He laughs.)* A man can't keep secrets from his wife. Believe me, I know!

Jekyll: Every person is a mystery, John. You are a mystery even to yourself.

Utterson: What is that supposed to mean?

Jekyll: Have you ever wanted to do something bad, even when you knew it was wrong?

Utterson: I suppose so. Everyone must have moments like that.

Jekyll: Exactly! There are two sides to every person. In most people, the good side is stronger than the bad side. But that doesn't mean the evil side isn't there, waiting for a chance to come out.

Utterson: Hmm, that's a very interesting idea that I'd like to talk about more. But it's late. I'll leave you two lovebirds to talk of more important things than good and evil.

Jekyll *(rising)*: I'm afraid you'd better go too, Jane. I have some important work that I must really finish.

Jane: Oh, Henry, not again!

Jekyll *(sighing)*: My work is nearly done. I promise that once we're married, I'll be a good husband. I'll never go into my laboratory after dark.

Jane *(smiling)*: You had better keep that promise, Henry Jekyll!

How would you describe Henry Jekyll?

Scene 2

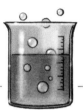

Narrator: It is one hour later. Dr. Jekyll is in his basement laboratory surrounded by test tubes. Jekyll pours a red liquid into a large glass. He adds a teaspoon of white powder.

Jekyll *(excitedly)*: This is the moment I've been waiting for! My months of hard work have finally come to an end!

Narrator: The liquid changes from red to purple to green. It starts to bubble. Jekyll picks up the glass and pours the green liquid down his throat.

Jekyll *(clutching his throat)*: Aaah! It burns! My insides are on fire! The room is spinning. Everything is turning dark and—

Narrator: Jekyll falls to the floor and passes out.

Ten minutes later, Dr. Jekyll wakes up—as Mr. Hyde.

Hyde *(excited)*: What's happened to me? There's long hair all over my hands! My fingernails have grown long and sharp like claws! What does the rest of me look like? I must see.

Narrator: Hyde looks at himself in a large mirror against the wall. He sees a bent, ugly man with long hair, crooked teeth, and cruel, cunning eyes.

Hyde: So this is the evil side of Jekyll that I hide from the world. Ha! That's what I'll call myself—Hyde! Edward Hyde!

Narrator: Hyde pauses and looks around the laboratory.

Hyde: This stuffy laboratory is no place for a fellow like me. The night is still young. I'm going out to have some fun!

Narrator: Hyde tries to open the door to the street. It's locked.

Hyde *(angrily):* That fool Jekyll! He didn't think it would be safe to let his evil side go

out! If I go upstairs to the front door, the servants are sure to see me. Darn Jekyll! I'll fix him!

Narrator: Hyde begins to break the test tubes and glasses. After a while, he falls to the floor, exhausted. When he wakes up, the mixture has worn off. Mr. Hyde has changed back into Dr. Jekyll.

Jekyll (looking around at the mess): So, everything I thought is actually true! I must continue to experiment and learn more about my evil side. But I must be careful. No one must learn the truth about Mr. Hyde!

Why do you think Jekyll locks Hyde inside the lab?

Scene 3

Narrator: It is the next morning. Dr. Jekyll is walking upstairs from his laboratory. He meets Poole, his butler, in the hallway.

Jekyll: Good morning, Poole. You look white as a ghost. Is something wrong?

Poole: I should ask you that question, Doctor. Minnie and I heard awful noises coming from your laboratory last night. We almost called the police.

Jekyll *(angrily)*: I've told you not to interfere when I'm working in my laboratory!

Poole: I'm sorry. But we thought someone had broken in. We thought you were in danger.

Jekyll: I promise you that it won't happen again. Oh, by the way, Poole, there's a gentleman who will be visiting me now and then. I'd like you to make a copy of the key to the laboratory door for him. That way, he can come and go as he pleases.

Poole: Very well, Dr. Jekyll. And what is the gentleman's name?

Jekyll: Edward Hyde.

Why do you think Jekyll decides to give Hyde his own key?

Scene 4

Narrator: It is several weeks later. Jane Manners is sitting in a restaurant. John Utterson enters.

Utterson *(sitting down at Jane's table)*: I came as soon as I got your message, Jane. You've been crying! What's the matter?

Jane: It's Henry. He won't see anyone. He spends all his time locked up in his laboratory. When he does come out, he seems very troubled.

Utterson: That isn't like Henry at all.

Jane: But that's not the worst part. Poole says there is an awful man named Edward Hyde who's been staying at the house. He goes out at night and comes in at the oddest hours. Poole thinks this Hyde has some hold over Henry.

Utterson *(frowning)*: I'm afraid Poole is right.

Narrator: Utterson removes a paper from his pocket and pushes it across the table.

Utterson: This is Henry's new will. He had me draw it up for him. It says that if Henry should die or disappear, all his money should go to this Mr. Hyde.

Jane *(worried)*: Why would Henry disappear?

Why do you think Jekyll wants his money to go to Hyde if anything happens?

Scene 5

Narrator: It is two hours later. Hyde has returned to Jekyll's house. He is trying to find his key to the laboratory. Sir Rodney Carew passes by.

Sir Rodney: What do you think you're doing here?

Hyde: I'm trying to get into my house, old man. Now get away before I lose my temper.

Sir Rodney: Liar! I know for a fact that this is the house of Dr. Henry Jekyll.

Hyde: So what?

Sir Rodney: Dr. Jekyll is a respectable man. He'd have nothing to do with a character like you. You have no key to this place! You're trying to break in!

Hyde: I told you to mind your own business!

Narrator: Hyde lifts his walking stick and begins to beat Sir Rodney savagely over the head again and again.

Sir Rodney: Stop! You're hurting me! Help! Someone!

Narrator: Minnie, Jekyll's maid, hears the screams. She looks out an upstairs window.

Minnie: Help! Police! Murder!

Narrator: Hyde finds the right key. He unlocks the door and rushes into the laboratory. On the street lies the lifeless body of Sir Rodney Carew.

How would you describe Hyde?

Scene 6

Narrator: It is 30 minutes later. A police officer is talking to Minnie outside the house.

Officer 1: Calm down now, Miss. Are you certain you know the man who killed Sir Rodney?

Minnie: Oh, yes. I saw his awful face clearly in the light of the street lamp. It was Dr. Jekyll's friend—Edward Hyde.

Narrator: A second officer comes out of the house.

Officer 2: We just searched the house. Dr. Jekyll doesn't seem to be home. The only room we couldn't get into was the laboratory. The door was locked.

Officer 1: The outside door to the laboratory is

locked as well. That's where Hyde must be! There's no way he can escape.

Narrator: The officers step up to the laboratory door and knock loudly.

Officer 2: Open up or we'll break down the door!

Narrator: There is a long silence. The door swings open slowly. There stands . . .

Minnie: Dr. Jekyll!

Jekyll *(calmly)*: Hello, Minnie. What are the police doing here? Is something wrong?

Officer 1: I'm afraid something is very wrong, Dr. Jekyll. A man was murdered in front of your house a short time ago. Your maid claims that the murderer came into the laboratory through this door.

Jekyll: That's impossible. I've been working here all evening. I saw no one.

Officer 2: Do you mind if we take a look around anyway?

Jekyll: Of course not.

Narrator: The police find no trace of Mr. Hyde.

Officer 1: Doctor, when is the last time you saw your friend, Mr. Hyde?

Jekyll: A few days ago.

Officer 2: Is there anywhere else you think we might find him?

Jekyll: I don't think you'll find him anywhere. I have a feeling that Mr. Hyde has gone away for good.

Officer 1: Oh, we'll find him. No one can get away with murder!

Why couldn't the police find Hyde?

Scene 7

Narrator: It is later that evening. Jekyll is alone in his laboratory.

Jekyll: Murder! How could I allow such a terrible thing to happen? I must have been mad. I was a fool to think I could control Edward Hyde. He ended up controlling me, but no more!

Narrator: Jekyll puts all his papers and books on the floor. Then he puts a match to the pile.

Jekyll: There! The formula for the mixture goes up in flames, and Hyde along with it. He will never return to do evil again! I am free of him. Free!

Narrator: There is a sudden knock on the door. Jane enters.

Jane: Henry, Poole just came to see me. The poor man was shaking with fear. He told me about Edward Hyde and the murder. It's too horrible!

Jekyll *(hugging her)*: Yes, Jane, but it's all over now. We are rid of Mr. Hyde forever.

Jane: How can you be so sure?

Jekyll: You'll just have to . . . *(in a low voice, like Hyde)* trust me.

Jane: Henry, are you all right? Your voice sounds so strange.

Jekyll: No, no! It's not possible! He can't come back! I haven't drunk the mixture!

Jane: What are you talking about? *(She gasps.)* Henry, look at your hands and face. Hair is growing all over them!

Hyde *(laughing)*: Does it upset you, dear?

Jane *(moving toward the door)*: Let me out of here, Henry!

Hyde: I can't let you go. You know too much. You'd tell the police everything.

Narrator: Hyde grabs Jane's throat with his clawed hands. He slowly squeezes her neck.

Jane: Henry, no! Please!

Hyde *(chuckling)*: Hyde, my dear. My name is Edward Hyde!

Why is Jekyll surprised when Hyde comes back?

Scene 8

Narrator: Seconds later, a shot rings out. Hyde lets go of Jane. He falls to the floor, with a bullet in his chest.

Officer 2 *(rushing in)*: Are you all right, Miss?

Officer 1 *(holding up a gun)*: I had no choice but to shoot him. I was standing outside the door in case Hyde returned. I heard your screams.

Narrator: Jane stares down at Hyde's dying body. The hair and claws disappear. Hyde changes back into Henry Jekyll.

Jane: Henry!

Jekyll: I'm sorry, Jane. Try to forgive me for the evil I've done. I thought I could control

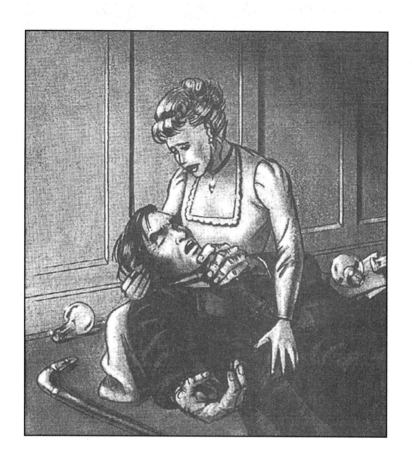

my evil side, but I was wrong. Edward Hyde has made Henry Jekyll's life unbearable.

Officer 2 *(shocked)*: I don't understand!

Officer 1: Who is he—Jekyll or Hyde?

Jekyll *(weakly)*: I am both—good and evil living inside the same body. And now, there is only one way that good can win out over evil.

Narrator: Henry grabs his chest.

Jekyll: Henry Jekyll's unhappy life must come to an end.

Narrator: Henry's eyes close. He dies in Jane's arms.

What is the only way for Jekyll to get rid of Hyde forever?

About the Author

Robert Louis Stevenson was born in Scotland in 1850. When he was young, Stevenson loved to read books, and he loved the open seas and adventure. As an adult, he moved a lot, hoping that a change of air would improve his health. He battled a lung disease his whole life. He and his family finally settled in the South Seas, where he lived until his death in 1894.

The books Stevenson wrote are full of adventure and suspense. *Treasure Island* started out as a pirate story Stevenson told his stepson, during a rainy school holiday. *The Strange Case of Dr. Jekyll and Mr. Hyde* was his second book. The idea for it came to him in a dream. He considered it the worst book he ever wrote. But it made him rich and famous.

Cover illustration by
Brad Walker

Interior illustrations by
Paul Didier

The Invisible Man

based on the classic story by
H.G. Wells

SCHOLASTIC INC.
New York   Toronto   London   Auckland   Sydney
Mexico City   New Delhi   Hong Kong

Characters

Narrator 1

Narrator 2

Griffin, a mysterious stranger

Mrs. Hall, the innkeeper

Millie, the chambermaid

Woman

Man

Dr. Cuss, a country doctor

Dr. Kemp, a scientist

Mrs. Farnum, Dr. Kemp's housekeeper

Sheriff

Narrator 1: One winter, out of the darkness, wind, and snow, a stranger appeared in our small village. What happened next has become a town legend.

Narrator 2: It all began when the man staggered into the Coach and Horses Inn. He was shouting.

Griffin: A fire! Give me a room and a fire! I am frozen solid!

Mrs. Hall: Sir . . . I . . . uh . . . sir. . .

Narrator 1: Mrs. Hall, a kindly lady who had run the inn for years, was stunned by the stranger's bizarre appearance. He was wrapped up from head to foot in rags. His hat, scarf and bug-like goggles hid every inch of his face, except for the pink tip of his nose.

Mrs. Hall: Sir, I . . . I can find a room for you. A room with a fireplace. But only if you have the money to pay for it.

Griffin: Money, ha! Will this help you find the room, madam?

Narrator 2: The stranger dropped some coins on the counter.

Mrs. Hall: Two gold pieces! Let me take your bags for you. Good gracious they are heavy. What's in here?

Griffin: Be careful with those, you fool. You could break my equipment. I am a scientist. Give me my bags.

Mrs. Hall: Let me take your coat and dry it out for you.

Griffin: DON'T TOUCH ME! I mean, I'm not warmed up yet.

Mrs. Hall: All right. But at least let me fix you something to eat.

Griffin: Fine. Just leave it on a tray outside the door of my room.

Scene 1

Narrator 1: One winter, out of the darkness, wind, and snow, a stranger appeared in our small village. What happened next has become a town legend.

Narrator 2: It all began when the man staggered into the Coach and Horses Inn. He was shouting.

Griffin: A fire! Give me a room and a fire! I am frozen solid!

Mrs. Hall: Sir . . . I . . . uh . . . sir. . .

Narrator 1: Mrs. Hall, a kindly lady who had run the inn for years, was stunned by the stranger's bizarre appearance. He was wrapped up from head to foot in rags. His hat, scarf and bug-like goggles hid every inch of his face, except for the pink tip of his nose.

Mrs. Hall: Sir, I . . . I can find a room for you. A room with a fireplace. But only if you have the money to pay for it.

Griffin: Money, ha! Will this help you find the room, madam?

Narrator 2: The stranger dropped some coins on the counter.

Mrs. Hall: Two gold pieces! Let me take your bags for you. Good gracious they are heavy. What's in here?

Griffin: Be careful with those, you fool. You could break my equipment. I am a scientist. Give me my bags.

Mrs. Hall: Let me take your coat and dry it out for you.

Griffin: DON'T TOUCH ME! I mean, I'm not warmed up yet.

Mrs. Hall: All right. But at least let me fix you something to eat.

Griffin: Fine. Just leave it on a tray outside the door of my room.

Narrator 1: Mrs. Hall heated up some soup for the stranger and asked Millie, the chambermaid, to bring it up to him. A few seconds later, Millie burst back into the kitchen. She looked terrified.

Mrs. Hall: Millie, what is it? What happened?

Millie: I knocked, but he didn't answer. So I opened his door. He looked up. Then he yanked his handkerchief to his mouth. But not before I saw . . .

Mrs. Hall: Saw what?

Millie: His mouth, Mrs. Hall, it . . it . . . wasn't there!

Mrs. Hall: It wasn't there?

Millie: It should have been. But instead there was a hole in his face. I mean no chin, no lips, no teeth. Just a black pit.

Mrs. Hall: Don't be ridiculous.

Millie: And that's not all. The rest of his head was completely wrapped in bandages, with only his nose sticking out.

Mrs. Hall: The poor man. He's probably been in a horrible accident.

Millie: Or maybe it's a disguise. Maybe he's a killer or an escapee from an insane asylum.

Mrs. Hall: That's enough, Millie.

What do you think is wrong with Griffin?

Scene 2

Narrator 2: The next morning, Mrs. Hall went upstairs to check on the strange visitor. When she entered his room, she was shocked.

Mrs. Hall: What's all this mess? Straw, splinters, broken glass. And what is that smell? It's disgusting!

Griffin: Look, I spilled a little carbolic acid over in the corner and . . .

Mrs. Hall: Acid! I don't want my floors ruined. I hope you plan on cleaning this up.

Griffin: Can't you see that I am busy? If the mess bothers you, put it on my bill. But if you interrupt me one more time, I'll . . .

Narrator 1: Mrs. Hall left the room before he could finish the threat.

Scene 3

Narrator 2: The winter months passed. The stranger stayed at the inn, working constantly. He paid his rent early. He hardly ever went out in the daylight. Soon, wild rumors about him were being whispered all over town.

Woman: My little girl saw him once and had nightmares for the rest of the week.

Man: The dogs snarl at him when he goes walking at night. But they are afraid to go near him.

Woman: I don't blame them. I think he's some kind of vampire.

Man: Of course he isn't a vampire. He's probably a runaway from a circus sideshow.

He has tattoos all over his body, I'll bet.

Woman: Maybe you're right. Maybe we ought to pity him.

Man: I don't know about that. He still might be dangerous.

Do you think Griffin is dangerous?
Why or why not?

Scene 4

Narrator 1: The village doctor, Dr. Cuss, was just as curious as anyone as to what was beneath the stranger's bandages. But he didn't like gossip. And as a scientist, his curiosity was more professional.

Narrator 2: Most of all, the doctor wondered what the stranger was doing in his room with all that equipment and all of those chemicals. So he went to the inn and climbed the stairs to pay the stranger a visit.

Narrator 1: From downstairs, Mrs. Hall heard a terrible scream. A moment later, Dr. Cuss rushed from the room, his face as pale as snow.

Dr. Cuss: Mrs. Hall, do I look like a crazy man? Do I?

Mrs. Hall: Of course not, Doctor. What happened? Catch your breath.

Dr. Cuss: I knocked on his door to see if I might help the poor fellow out. He must not have heard me. So I opened the door. When I came in, he was busy mixing chemicals. He tried to hide his hands in his pockets, but I saw them.

Mrs. Hall: What about them?

Dr. Cuss: Mrs. Hall, he had no hands. There were just gaping holes at the ends of his sleeves. Then he raised one sleeve right up to my face and I felt a thumb and a finger tweak my nose.

Mrs. Hall: Seriously?

Dr. Cuss: I was so startled that I smacked his sleeve with my hand. And I swear to you, there was an arm in there. But it was invisible!

How would you explain what Dr. Cuss saw upstairs in Griffin's room?

Scene **5**

Narrator 2: Dr. Cuss's story swept through the town, but few people really believed it. Then, one night, a bizarre burglary happened at the house of Reverend Bunting. After that, everyone in the town believed Dr. Cuss's story.

Woman: Did you hear about the break-in at the reverend's house? He was sound asleep in bed, when he was awakened by the sound of soft footsteps. He grabbed a poker and followed the sound . . .

Man: Yes! Then he saw the light from a candle moving around, and he heard his money being counted. So he walked toward the criminal. . .

Woman: But all he saw was an empty money drawer and a burning candle. Then comes the really creepy part . . .

Man: He heard someone laughing and saw the kitchen door open and close all by itself.

Woman: It must be that invisible stranger Dr. Cuss saw at the inn!

Do you think the woman is right about Griffin? Why or why not?

Scene 6

Narrator 1: When Mrs. Hall heard about the burglary she called the sheriff. When he arrived, Mrs. Hall and Millie took him to the stranger's room.

Mrs. Hall: This is his room. Don't knock. You'll warn him.

Sheriff: Right you are. Give me the key.

Narrator 2: The sheriff quietly unlocked the door, then slowly pushed it open.

Millie: Oh my . . . LOOK!

Mrs. Hall: It can't be.

Narrator 1: The three of them stared in disbelief at what they saw. No hands, no feet, no head. Just a bathrobe—floating in the air.

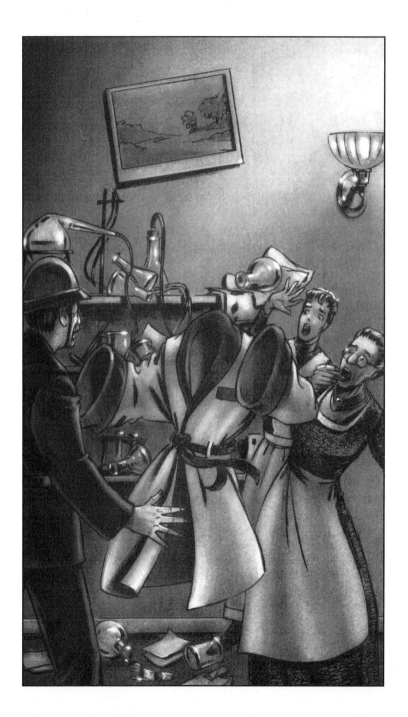

Sheriff: Well ghost, or man, or laundry—or whatever you are, you are going to jail!

Griffin: For what, Sheriff? Is it a crime to be invisible?

Sheriff: I am not arresting you for being invisible. I'm arresting you for burglary.

Griffin: You can't arrest what you can't see.

Narrator 2: The floating bathrobe dropped to the floor in a heap.

Narrator 1: Mrs. Hall heard a fist hit the sheriff in the face, then saw the sheriff fall backward, grabbing his jaw.

Mrs. Hall: You better not touch me, Griffin!

Griffin: I'll be back for you.

Do you think Griffin will get away?
Why or why not?

Scene 7

Narrator 2: At that very moment, Dr. Kemp, a scientist who lived on the other side of town, was reading the newspaper. He was reading an article about the so-called invisible man. He didn't believe a word of it because there was no scientific proof.

Narrator 1: The doorbell rang and Dr. Kemp's housekeeper rushed to answer it.

Dr. Kemp: Who was at the door, Mrs. Farnum?

Mrs. Farnum: I'm not sure, Doctor. When I answered it, there was no one outside. You don't suppose it's that invisible crazy man who's on the loose?

Dr. Kemp: Not that ridiculous idea again! It's probably kids playing a prank.

Mrs. Farnum: But the papers say he's out there hunting for his next victim. You heard about what he did to the sheriff and Mrs. Hall. Sometimes I think I feel his fingers tightening around my throat.

Dr. Kemp: My dear Mrs. Farnum, maybe you should take the rest of the day off. This hocus-pocus has really gotten to you. Go get some rest. If I have an invisible visitor, I'll calm him and make him happy with your cooking.

Why isn't Dr. Kemp afraid?

Scene 8

Narrator 2: Around midnight that night, Dr. Kemp went upstairs and noticed that his bed was rumpled, as if someone had slept in it. Then, he heard what sounded like a man snoring.

Dr. Kemp: Who's in here? Speak up!

Griffin: Is that you Kemp?

Dr. Kemp: Am I going crazy? Am I hearing things?

Griffin: No, Kemp. I'm the invisible man everyone has been talking about.

Dr. Kemp: This must be a trick.

Griffin: No trick, old boy. Hold your hand out. Can you feel that?

Narrator 1: Dr. Kemp held out his hand and felt another hand wrap around it. But he saw absolutely nothing.

Dr. Kemp: It's true! I can't believe it!

Griffin: Do you remember my voice, Kemp? We went to college together. I was the whiz kid in chemistry. They called me a genius.

Dr. Kemp: Is that you, Griffin? The albino? Did a chemical accident do this to you?

Griffin: It was no accident. It was an experiment that will make me the most powerful man on earth. But first, I must have food, drink, and clothes. Then I'll tell you everything.

How do you think Griffin plans to become the most powerful man on earth?

Scene **9**

Narrator 2: Dr. Kemp warmed up some of Mrs. Farnum's leftovers. He gave Griffin food and a pair of pajamas to wear. Then he settled down to listen to the most incredible story he'd ever heard.

Griffin: I first became interested in visible reflection because of my own weird coloring. Chalk-white skin and hair, with red eyes. Remember? They used to call me lab rat.

Dr. Kemp: I remember. That was very cruel.

Griffin: Ha! I'll show them cruel! But back to my story. I knew things must have color to reflect light. I also knew that the eye can only see what reflects light. So if I could withdraw all the color from living tissue. . . .

Dr. Kemp: Then you could be invisible.

Griffin: Exactly! I worked for months on animals. I made a kitten almost completely invisible except for two glowing eyes that followed me everywhere. But it distracted me and I had to get rid of it.

Dr. Kemp: How awful!

Griffin: I finally got the chemical mixture just right. And I took it myself. As you can see—I mean *not* see—I am a genius.

Dr. Kemp: So why have you come to me?

Griffin: I need your help. My work is not complete. As it is, animals can still smell me. My food shows until it is completely digested. And I need invisible clothes to keep me warm. I was making progress until those snoops at the inn ruined it. But I'll have my revenge.

Dr. Kemp: Isn't that a bit extreme?

Griffin: Of course not! I plan to get rid of Mrs. Hall and then everyone will do as I say. They're already terrified of me. Think of the power I'll have. Think of the money I'll have.

Dr. Kemp: Uh . . .yes, of course.

Griffin: See, I knew you'd listen to reason. But now I must sleep. Don't betray me, or you'll be my first example!

How do you think Dr. Kemp feels about Griffin's plan?

Scene 10

Narrator 1: Dr. Kemp knew he had to act quickly. He gave a neighbor's servant a note to take to the sheriff. Then, he waited for Griffin to wake up, praying that the sheriff would get there in time to stop Griffin before he began killing.

Griffin: Good morning, Kemp.

Dr. Kemp: What? Oh, I didn't see you. I mean, I can't see you.

Griffin: You seem a bit jumpy. Did you think over what I said last night?

Dr. Kemp: Yes. But I have some questions. Why does there have to be killing?

Griffin: To keep people under my power. To show them I am an invincible invisible man.

Dr. Kemp: As your partner, I'm not sure I approve. Here's your breakfast, Griffin.

Narrator 2: Griffin took several bites of toast, but dropped it back on his plate when he heard the sound of footsteps approaching.

Griffin: Listen, someone's here.

Dr. Kemp: It's . . .uh . . . probably my housekeeper, Mrs. Farnum.

Griffin: No, it's not, you traitor!

Narrator 1: At that moment, the sheriff walked in the front door.

Sheriff: OK, Kemp. Where is he?

Dr. Kemp: He's here. Oh, no! Watch out. He's throwing that tray right at you.

Narrator 2: But before the sheriff could duck, the metal tray hit him right in the head. The sheriff grabbed his head and groaned.

Dr. Kemp: Hurry. We've got to catch him before he starts killing.

Sheriff: But how can we track him down when we can't see him?

Dr. Kemp: He gave me some clues to that himself. The bit of toast he ate should still show for a few hours. And if you have any dogs, they may be able to sniff him out from his scent on the sheets.

Why did Dr. Kemp pretend to be Griffin's partner?

Scene 11

Narrator 1: Dr. Kemp and the sheriff chased Griffin all day. The hounds had his scent. And several people reported seeing the toast in his stomach. But the invisible man stayed one step ahead of them all day.

Narrator 2: That night, Dr. Kemp found a note that had been slipped under his door. It read: For a whole day, I have been chased like an animal. But now I've digested and now the animal is coming for you, traitor! You will be the first to die in my reign of terror. Happy death day! Signed, the invisible man.

Narrator 1: Kemp locked his doors and waited for the attack. Suddenly, he heard a window breaking downstairs. The next thing he knew there was a large red ax swinging at him. He

dodged it and screamed for help.

Dr. Kemp: Sheriff, help! He's here!

Narrator 2: The sheriff, who had been hiding in the closet the whole time, heard Dr. Kemp's call for help and jumped out.

Sheriff: I'm here Kemp. Where is he? What's happening?

Dr. Kemp: He's . . . gah . . . strangling me! Help!

Sheriff: Try to hold still.

Narrator 1: The sheriff fired his pistol. Griffin screamed.

Dr. Kemp: You got him!

Sheriff: Careful. He could be faking.

Dr. Kemp: No, I can feel his blood.

Griffin: I'm dying. Me, the invincible . . . invisible . . .

Dr. Kemp: He's not breathing. I can't hear his heartbeat. What a waste!

Sheriff: What do you mean, waste?

Dr. Kemp: It's a waste that such a brilliant discovery was made by such a twisted mind. We'll never know what good it might have done. The secret dies with him.

Why didn't the invisible man want to use his discovery to help people?

About the Author

H.G. Wells was born in England in 1866. Some people say his love of reading and writing began when he broke his leg as a child. He spent his rest period reading books.

Wells studied science at a time when many discoveries were being made. He liked to write about things that hadn't been invented yet, like airplanes and submarines.

One book he wrote, *The War of the Worlds*, was a story about Martians invading the Earth. In 1938, the story was broadcast as a radio drama. Many people panicked when they heard it. They thought it was really happening!